Britain so the Home Guard helped out on air raid duty and practised their fighting skills.

Women wanted to join the Home Guard but the government wouldn't let them. Thousands of women formed themselves into the Women's Home Defence Movement and arranged their own training.

Enrolment form for the Home Guard.

MINISTRY OF LABOUR AND NATIONAL SERVICE

DEFENCE (HOME GUARD) REGULATIONS, 1940

Direction to enrol in the Home Guard.

To: Mr. H. E. Potts, SPRINGFIELD ROAD,
110ᵗʰ Vicarage Rd CHELMSFORD.
CHELMSFORD ESSEX.

26 AUG '42 (Date)

In pursuance of Regulation 31(1) of the Defence (Home Guard) Regulations, 1940, I, the undersigned, National Service Officer within the meaning of the Defence (General) Regulations, 1939, do hereby direct you to enrol in the Home Guard and for that purpose to present yourself at Lamarsh House Mildmay Rd CHELMSFORD (place)

on 14 SEP '42 Match between 10pm and 9pm (time)

National Service Officer.

Note 1.—Any person failing to comply with a direction under the Defence (Home Guard) Regulations, 1940, is liable on summary conviction to imprisonment for a term not exceeding three months or to a fine not exceeding £100 or to both such imprisonment and such fine. There are heavier penalties for conviction on indictment.

Note 2.—Any person desiring to apply for the withdrawal or modification of a direction on the ground that it would be an exceptional hardship if he were required to enrol in the Home Guard, may do so by making an application to the National Service Officer on the appropriate form which may be obtained from the Local Office of the Ministry of Labour and National Service. Such application must be made within four days of the giving of the direction. If such an application is made within the period stated, the person to whom the direction is made is not bound to comply with the direction as suspended until a further communication is received from the National Service Officer.

C.D. 447.

Invasion!

Hitler planned to invade Britain by sea but first he had to defeat the Royal Air Force (RAF) so that his troops could land without being attacked from the air.

The Luftwaffe (the German air force) attacked ports, airfields, radar stations and aircraft factories. The RAF and the Luftwaffe tried to shoot each other down in the 'Battle of Britain'. After about eight weeks Britain was judged to have won because the Luftwaffe lost three times as many planes as the RAF.

Lookout!

Look out for aircraft used in the Battle of Britain in aircraft and war museums. Find out what you score on page 14.

Hitler gave up his plan to invade by sea and decided to bomb Britain instead (the Blitz). He tried to bring life to a halt by attacking places such as military targets, gas and power stations, the docks and railways, factories, telephone exchanges and even hospitals.

WILLS'S CIGARETTES

REPRESENTATION OF AIR DEFENCE CONTROL ROOM

An artist's impression of the control room where all the defence on air attacks was planned.

On duty

First Hitler bombed London. Then he attacked 15 other cities such as Portsmouth, Liverpool, Coventry, Plymouth, Birmingham, Glasgow and Bristol.

me mum told me to save this space mister!

Thousands were killed by direct hits from bombs. People took shelter in subways, the London Underground and air raid shelters until the raid was over. If people knew a raid was likely, they queued up or sent children in advance to save a space. Many awoke to find their homes had been destroyed.

Beating the INVADER

A MESSAGE FROM THE PRIME MINISTER

Messages like these helped people to believe in what they were fighting for.

IF invasion comes, everyone—young or old, men and women—will be eager to play their part worthily.

GIVE ALL THE HELP YOU CAN TO OUR TROOPS

STAND FIRM

A whole 'army' of people were on duty during the Blitz. The Air Raid Precautions wardens (ARP) checked to see if people were all right in shelters. Police, nurses, doctors and fire services went to the scene of explosions. Soldiers were called in to defuse unexploded bombs and clear up the damage.

Lookout!

Look out for displays about the Blitz in war museums. Find out what you score on page 14.

Women belonging to the Women's Voluntary Service (WVS) ran mobile canteens or helped bombed-out families to find somewhere to stay. Everyone helped to dig out people buried alive.

Put your lights out!

One of the most important duties the ARP had was making sure people obeyed the blackout rules.

The Luftwaffe mostly attacked at night when it was more difficult to shoot down enemy planes. So from the beginning of the war everyone had to 'black out' all lights to make it more difficult for German pilots to see their targets.

Q: Who invented fire?

A: Some bright spark!

Put that light out !

Lookout!

Look out for your local fire station. Find out what you score on page 14.

Every night people had to hang heavy curtains or tape black card to their windows to make sure that no light escaped from their house. They had to remember to switch lights off before they stepped outside and to cover torches and bike headlamps. The few buses, lorries and cars on the streets were fitted with special headlights that gave off very little light.

WILLS'S CIGARETTES

REMOVAL OF INCENDIARY BOMB WITH SCOOP AND HOE

This card showed people how to get rid of an incendiary bomb with a shovel!

To overcome the blackout German planes would drop incendiary (fire) bombs to start fires and light up areas so that they could see their targets. This made the job of the fire service very important in the war.

Land girls

Farmers had a vital job in the war. They had to produce as much food as possible. Without them food shortages would have been far worse.

When war broke out most young men who worked on farms went away to fight. So the government encouraged women to join the Land Army to help out. Land girls, as they were known, wore a hat, jodhpurs, overalls and, in winter, a warm overcoat.

Land girls often complained that the clothes they were given to work in weren't fashionable enough!

Many land girls came from cities and had never been on a farm before. Despite this, they learned to drive tractors, plough the land, sow and harvest crops, look after animals, service machinery and cut down trees. Many farmers said they were the best help they had ever had!

Q: Why was the farmer cruel?

A: Because he pulled the corn by its ears!

Lookout!

Look out for a farm. Find out what you score on page 14.

Children helped out in school holidays and factory workers gave up their spare time to work on farms. Prisoners-of-war were often used for farm work too.

Factory workers

Most factories had to change the products they made in peace time to things used in war. Some factories were specially built to make war equipment.

Factories making fabric were very important because cloth was needed for making uniforms, parachutes, hospital bedding and camouflage.

During the war many women chose to work in factories and helped to build parts for aircraft, tanks, ships and weapons. Like land girls, they took on jobs previously done by men. Because more war equipment was desperately needed, factory girls had to work long hours – and often had to look after children as well.

When you get home ...

... search for these WWII words. Don't forget to look backwards and diagonally too.

AIR RAID
LUFTWAFFE
RAF
WVS
ARP
HITLER
LAND ARMY
BLITZ
FACTORY
INVASION

Lookout!

Look out for a factory built before WWII. Find out what you score on page 14.

L	A	R	P	W	X	H	S	I
U	A	I	R	R	A	I	D	N
F	G	N	H	A	T	T	M	V
T	O	R	D	F	E	L	O	A
W	V	S	B	A	C	E	B	S
A	B	D	L	F	R	R	P	I
F	J	O	I	K	T	M	C	O
F	A	C	T	O	R	Y	Y	N
E	T	V	Z	E	H	R	Z	O

How to use the sticke

First find what you've go
Then peel off a stick
and stick it in the blar

No part of this publicati
be reproduced by any means
without prior
permission of
Newbery & England.

Text: Elizabeth Newbery.

Design: Linda Francis.

Main illustrations:
© Clinton Banbury.

Images © and by kind
permission: p2 and 6 Miss B
Pillow; p4 and 8 Mr D Stocker;
p9 Miss M Ward.

Production: N&E.

Publication in this form
© Jarrold Publishing
(Pitkin Guides), 2003,
latest reprint 2006.

Pitkin Guides is an imprint of
Jarrold Publishing, Norwich.

Concept & text:
© N&E 2003,
3 North St, Osney Island,
Oxford OX2 0AY.

ISBN 13: 978-1-84165-121-7

ISBN 10: 1-84165-121-4   3/06

Surna
First
Names
Full postal address

· · · · · · · · · ·
· · · · · · · · · ·
· · · · · · · · · ·
· · · · · · · · · ·
· · · · · · · · · ·

Fill in above with
block capitals only

FOR OFFICIAL ENTRY ONLY (apart from Holder's Signature)
ANY OTHER ENTRY OR ANY ALTERATION, MARKING OR
ERASURE IS PUNISHABLE BY A FINE OR IMPRISONMENT
OR BOTH.